A CONNEAUT CHRISTMAS

E.M. CHAMBERS

PAGE PUBLISHING
Conneaut Lake, PA

First originally published by Page Publishing 2023

ISBN 979-8-88793-431-0 (pbk)
ISBN 979-8-88793-434-1 (digital)

Printed in the United States of America

To Uncle Frank Amuso, the true heart of our family

Many years ago, as the winter season approached,

the hunt for my first job was about to broach.

Holiday Postal Workers Needed, the sign read,

and onward I went fast in my stead.

After a brief but tense interview with Postman Hunklefelp,

I was Conneaut Lake Post's new holiday help.

As the Thanksgiving holiday passed,
the Christmas season was in full blast.
There were packages in, packages out.
So many packages going about.

It was a busy but happy
time to work.
Everyone was feeling
the Christmas perk.
Patrons come in beaming
with their stories to tell
as they sent and received their
packages through the mail.

Mr. Bell was sending his grandson Ben a train. It was his first Christmas away from his family in Lake Champlain.

Ms. Lavender proudly noted that the fancy package she had received was a new teapot from her sister Genevieve.

On December 3, a day I won't forget,
a very interesting gentleman
came onto our set.
He gave me a start and
brought me to attention.
He had a round middle and a
beard too long not to mention.
His face was kind with
sparkling eyes so bright
that matched his rosy cheeks just right.

"I have a package," he said, holding up a ticket for me.

I found he did indeed had three!

All small and postmarked from different places—Pittsburgh, Portland, and Tallahassee.

"Thanks, Nick!" he said, and out he went

with a cold gust following his scent.

Conneaut Lake being a small town
with lots of people who like to "know the news going 'round."
I found out that Mr. Amuso had retired to settle
in Conneaut Lake from one gossiping rebel.

According to Ms. Lavender,
he was a good sort
when it came to neighbors as
she noted with a snort.
With her news that was
never a bummer,
I knew that he led the Hazel Park
golf tournament last summer.

Mr. Amuso became of interest
to me over that month.
Every few days he came in with a hunch
that he had a package, and in
fact, it would be a bunch.
Always polite with a twinkle in his eye.
I thought he must be a very special guy.
His packages came from all over the place
from Canada, West Virginia, and LaPlace.
I found myself wondering, what is
his story? What could he be?
A secret agent, diplomat, or quite possibly…

The time did pass, and December rattled on
until it came to Christmas Eve, the night things go on.
The night was cold and things were getting boring
when one package fell soaring.
It was addressed to Mr. Amuso, much to my foe.
I forgot it with his pickup two hours ago.
In that moment, it hit me

how sad he would be to miss this last present under his tree.

That thought I couldn't bear

to just leave that special package there.

I would take it to him before Christmas with time to spare!

I closed up shop for the night,
and off I went with all my might.
I started my drive through the sleepy town of Conneaut Lake,
taking in the town's beauty in my wake,
passing the shops closed tight for the night.

11

I saw the *Barbara J* setting, sailing out of sight,
taking her last tour of the lake as the Christmas tree lights
my breath did take.
It's a beautiful town and a lovely sight
on this cold December night.

I made my way to Mohawk drive
and found that I had quickly arrived.
It was a neat blue-roofed house with significant space
and a sign in front that said "Our Place."
I could see smoke coming from the
chimney
and the light inside flickering
with whimsy.

For a second, I thought, *Nick, you are crazy*.

But something pulled me to that house and made me hazy.

With my one nerve of steel, I went to knock on the door,

And in an instant, he stood there on the floor.

Appearing before me, he was with a smile on his face

and his twinkling eyes forming a memory I dare not erase.

He said, "Hello, Nick! Glad you made it alright. I was expecting you tonight!"

Mr. Amuso had turned, almost taking flight,

to open the package I had brought him this night.

I took in the room with a cozy fire

to find a yellow cat sitting up like a sire.

Mr. Amuso turned, very pleased,

holding up an ornament for me to see.

It was a yellow cat with a ribboned bell tied on its neck

that shone like gold against the ribbon's check.

As he went to hang it up for all to see,

he said, "Thanks so much for helping me complete my tree!

You must have been curious as I am sure I would be

at the number of packages I did receive.

To solve that mystery, I need to explain

that being away from my family causes my heart much pain.

You see, this is the year I retire in search of new friend I hope to inspire

to lead on the work I so admire.

To help me in my quest

and to celebrate as I do best,

my family and friends have made ornaments to send,

each one reminding me of each dear friend."

I couldn't help but smile at his explanation,

admitting my curiosity as was his expectation.

He offered me a cup of Christmas tea,

for which I took gladly, you see.

To make a friend, you have to extend a courtesy.

It was the love and kindness of all those people he had met

who helped him to never forget.

No matter where he went or would be,
their thoughts and prayers with him would be
reviving the true meaning of family.

That night as we sat and talked of his travels,

I finally saw the last of his plan unravel…

As I was the person he meant to inspire

to start my life journey as he would inquire.

Now as I look back on that day, with joy in my heart,

I only hope on this night to impart

this lesson of love and light and to you all good night…

ABOUT THE AUTHOR

Emily Chambers is an accomplished internal medicine physician who currently practices on the North Side of Pittsburgh. She started her work in the literary world as a children's book illustrator just out of high school illustrating three children's books and one book cover. In addition to her medical and literary work, she is also a wife to her loving husband, Brent, and the proud mom to her twin sons, Jackson and Maximus, and daughter, Sydney Rae. She describes herself as a creative soul loving painting, crafting, cooking, and spending time with her family.

Ingram Content Group UK Ltd.
Milton Keynes UK
UKRC031054230323
419045UK00001B/7

9798887934310